LOUIS
Red Letter Day
by metaphrog

LOUIS FELT AS IF HE HAD NOT WRITTEN TO ANYONE FOR AGES. HE FELT IT DID HIM GOOD TO WRITE.

PERHAPS THAT WAS WHY HE WAS IN GOOD SPIRITS. OR, PERHAPS, IT WAS BECAUSE HE HAD TAKEN TIME OVER HIS APPEARANCE.

IT WASN'T REALLY SOMETHING THAT LOUIS BOTHERED ABOUT. THE WAY THINGS LOOKED. PERHAPS THAT WAS WHY HE WASN'T GETTING ON AS WELL AS HE WOULD HAVE LIKED.

SOMEHOW, WRITING TOOK HIM OUT OF THE WORLD. OUT OF HIMSELF. EVEN A LETTER.

LOUIS
Red Letter Day
by metaphrog

The publisher acknowledges support
from Creative Scotland towards
the publication of this title

Graphic Novel

ISBN 9780954598426

www.metaphrog.com

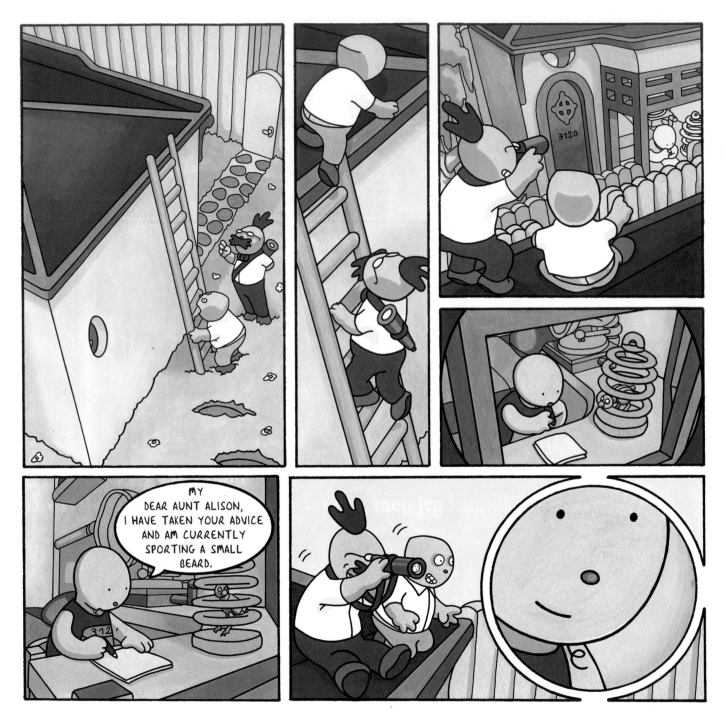

8

THE SECOND BELL MEANT IT REALLY WAS TIME TO GET BACK TO THE MACHINE. LOUIS UNDERSTOOD THE IMPORTANCE OF HIS WORK. EVERYBODY NEEDS AIR TO BREATHE, THEY HAD SAID. IT WAS HARD TO ARGUE WITH THAT.

EVERYONE NEEDS FOOD TO EAT. AND SO ON...

SOMETIMES THINGS DIDN'T RUN SMOOTHLY.

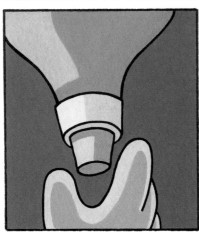

17

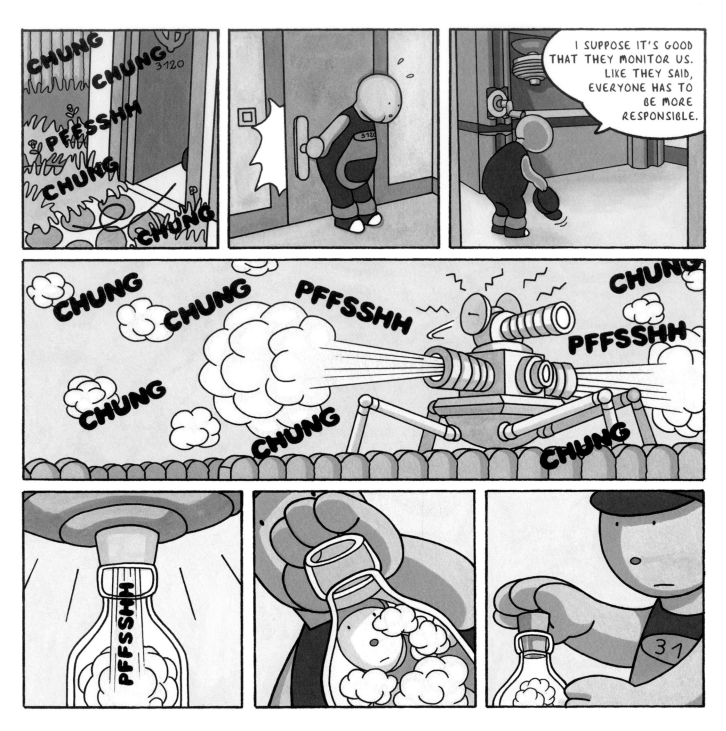

LOUIS WAS USED TO THE NOISES OF HIS MACHINE AND EVEN WITH HIS SENSITIVE HEARING THIS SOUND HAD CEASED TO BOTHER HIM. IN FACT THE VIBRATIONS TICKLED HIS HEARING MEMBRANES. HE REMEMBERED HIS PARENTS EXPLAINING TO HIM THAT HIS HEAD WAS LIKE A MICROPHONE.

HE HADN'T BEEN SURE IF HE LIKED THE SOUND OF THAT.

DING DONG

AT LAST, THE CHANGE-OVER BELL. IT WAS TIME FOR LOUIS TO SWITCH TO VEGETABLES.

SEALANT RESIN DRIES FAST

19

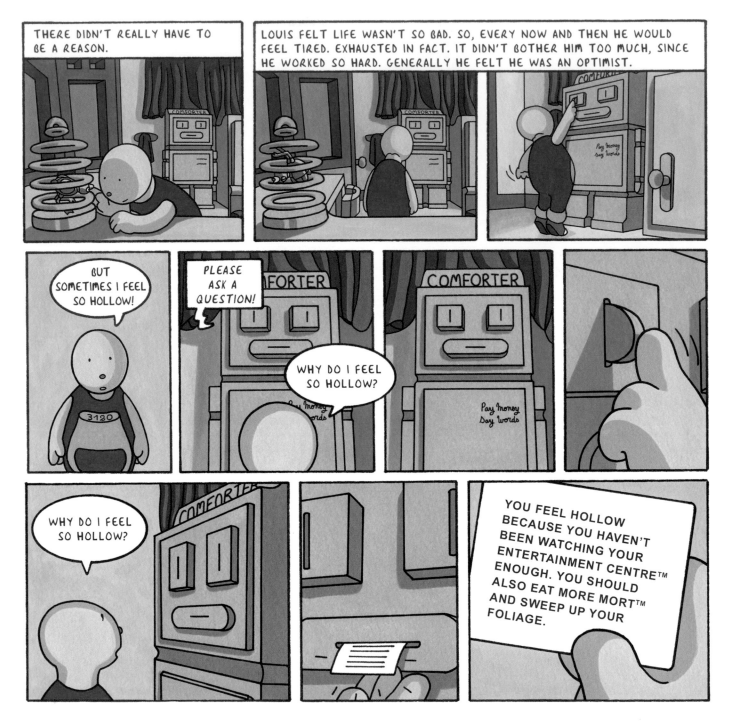

LOUIS BRIEFLY WONDERED HOW THE COMFORTER KNEW ABOUT HIS MESSY GARDEN.

I'M PROBABLY ALL CONFUSED.

... NIGHT HAMLET. AND REMEMBER: TONIGHT IS A LONESOME TOWN.

HIS BODY FELT HEAVY. FUNNY TO BE HEAVY AND HOLLOW. BUT HE COULDN'T LAUGH.

THAT NIGHT LOUIS SLEPT FEVERISHLY. HE DREAMT OF THE MARVELLOUS INSECT.

POC

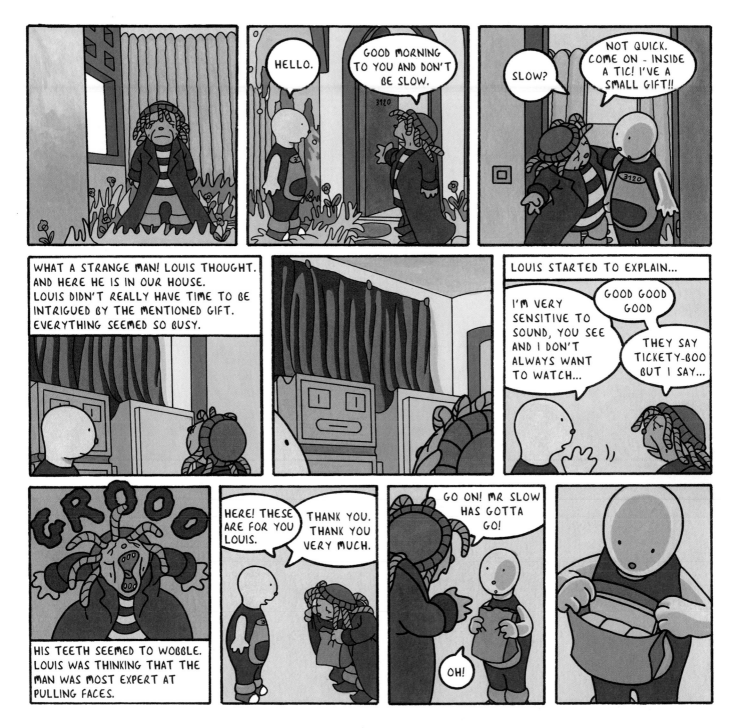

LOUIS THOUGHT ABOUT THE MYSTERIOUS STRANGER AND THEN ABOUT THE MOUNTAINS. THE STRANGER LOOKED, LOUIS IMAGINED, LIKE THE SORT OF PERSON WHO WOULD HAVE EXPLORED THE WORLD.

LOUIS WISHED HE'D HAD TIME TO ASK HIM. PERHAPS HE CAME FROM FAR AWAY.

ONCE MORE LOUIS FOUND HIMSELF DAYDREAMING.

32

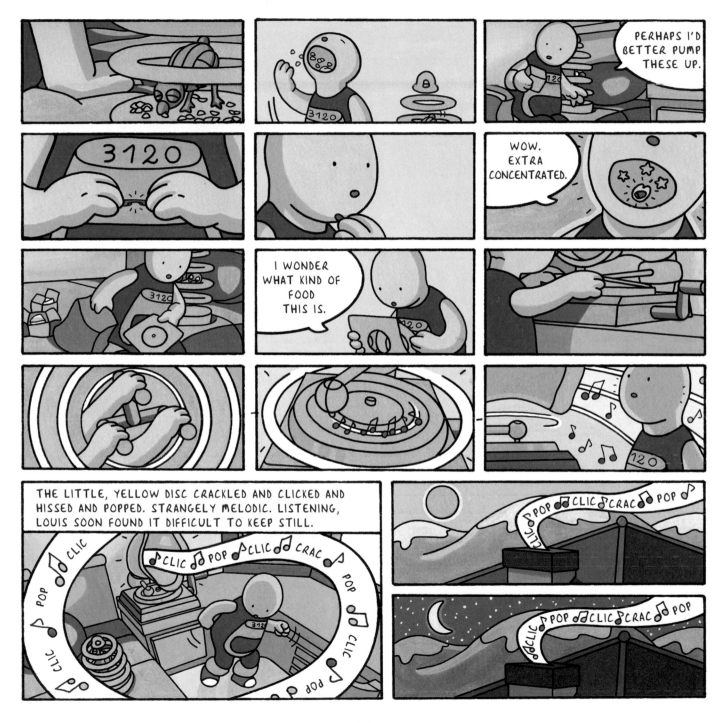

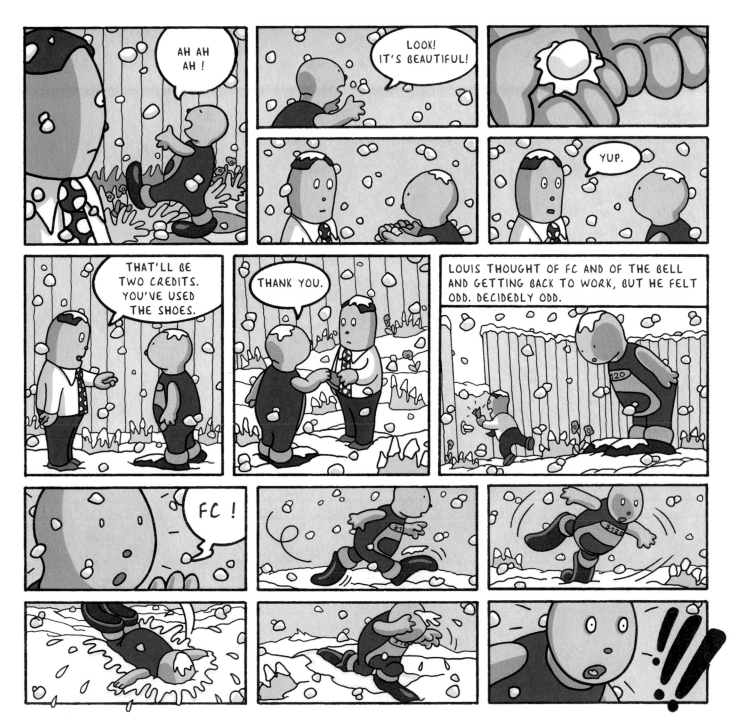

44

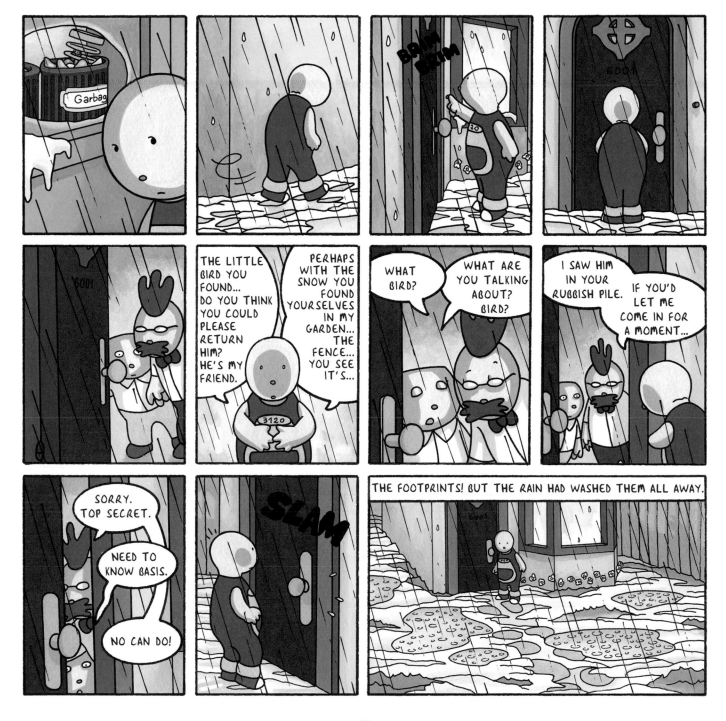

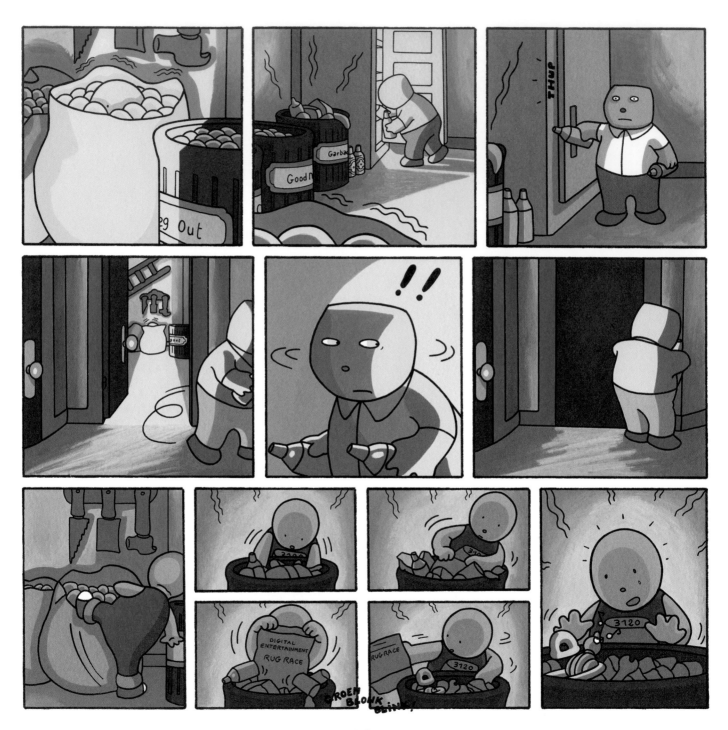

LOUIS DECIDED HE COULDN'T JUST LEAVE FC INSIDE.

CLIC ♪ POP ♪ CLIC ♪

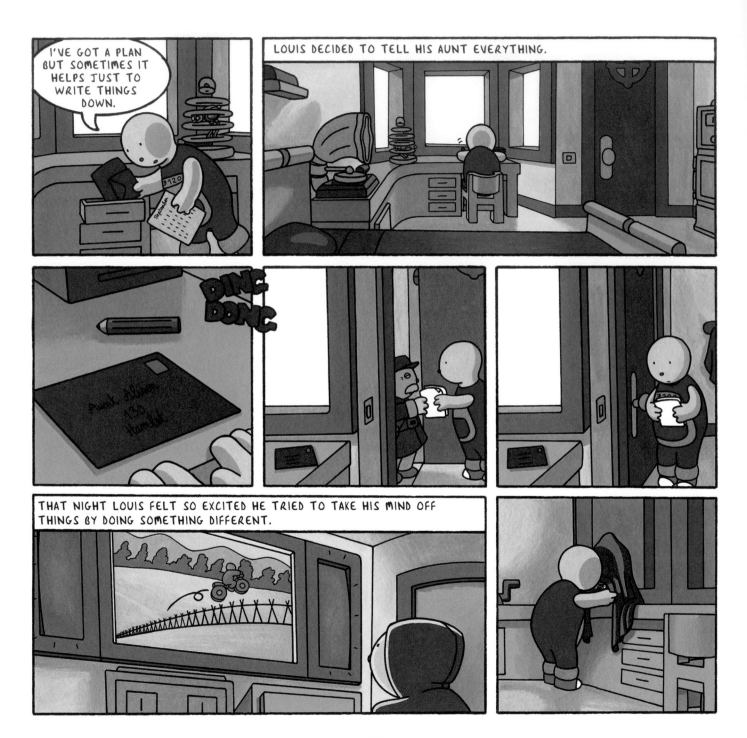

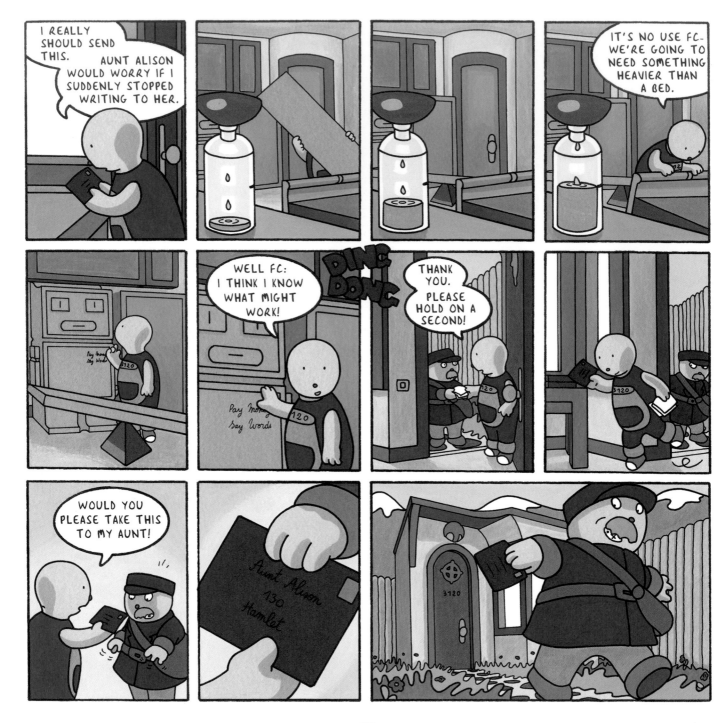

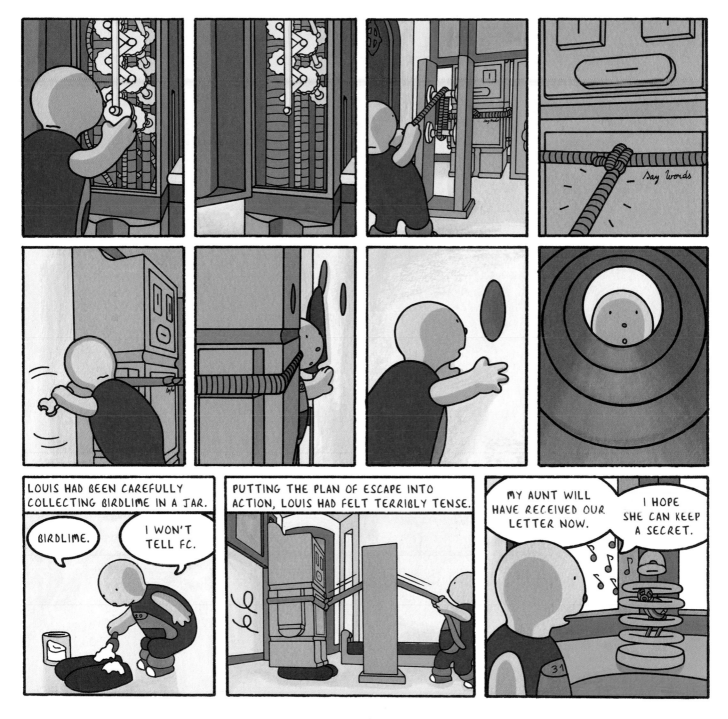

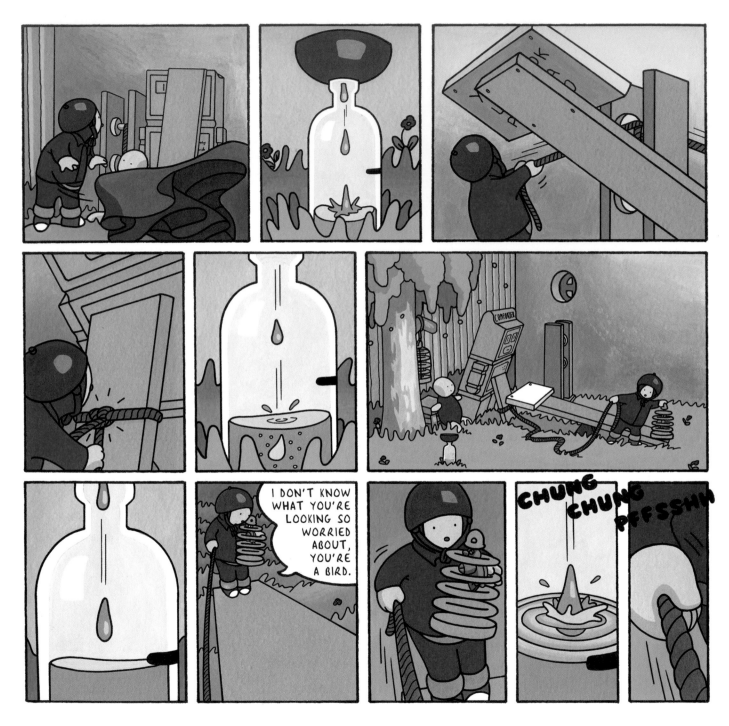

The Making
of Louis

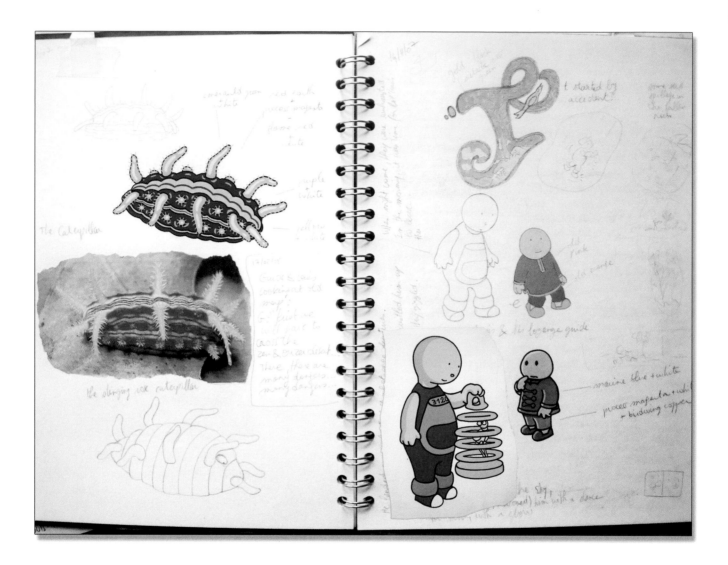

Origin of a story in pictures:

character designs and ideas in sketchbooks.

Preparing a story in words:

gathering notes and ideas.

[They get up and huddle together.]

[One whispers something in the other's ear and then they go back conspiratorially into their own house. Where we see them explicitly completing the practical joke involving Louis. Completing the letter the manipulative neighbour gestures exaggeratedly as the other writes and then we fade to shadowy outside. They are also preparing a pile of letters and prospectuses, this involves putting a large amount of them in a bag in an untidy manner.]

[To build up the neighbours' characters, the blockhead with the square head says "shiny" - they both laugh.]
N1: Shiny!
Both: Hahahahah

[Cut back to Louis at his desk writing his letter.]

N: Louis realised he wasn't particularly good at writing but he had the opinion that he wasn't particularly good at anything. He wouldn't bother to mention the moustache part because it seemed sensible that it went with a beard.

[Louis talks to himself while he's writing.]

L: It isn't unpleasant at all except when I sense it growing. But this is probably in my imagination.

[Cut away from Louis, again use an arial view, via a panel where he is viewed from outside the window from the relative view point of his neighbours' house.]
closeup to Q & J with letter
[Another panel, inside neighbours' house, as we see Louis' neighbours, one is helping the other into the jacket of a postman's uniform.]

[A false moustache and a cap completes the disguise as the neighbour receives a slap on the back from his cohort who is covering his mouth almost engulfed by laughter. The scheming neighbour leads the dafter one, dressed up as the postman, to the gate and towards Louis' gate. Here we see him pick up a spider from its web and say:]

N1: Shiny.
[As he pops the big, fat spider into his mouth.

[Back to Louis' room as he thoughtfully seals the letter with a small wax stamp. Take a few panels to do this, with the narrative staggered across it, as it allows for the neighbour to arrive as the false postman.]

N: Louis knew that his mind could be his own worst enemy but he did not know that he had an aunt.

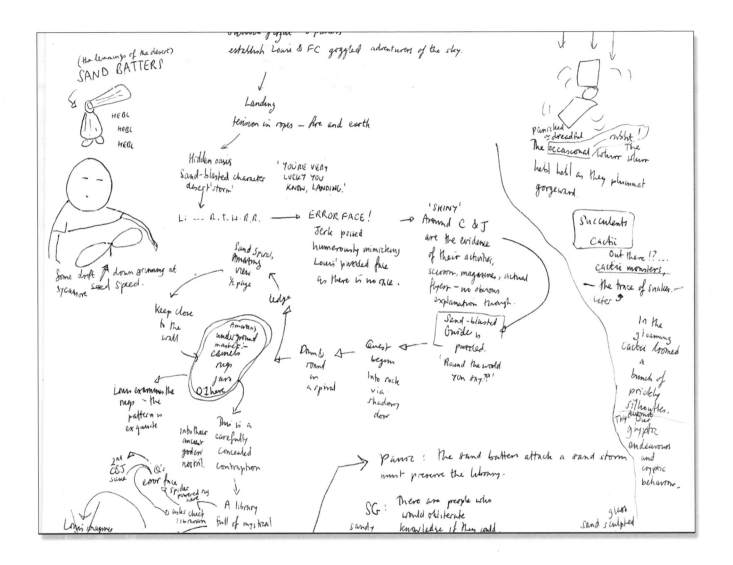

Planning the story.

Left: a page of script from Louis - Red Letter Day.

Above: schematic diagram for the structure of a story
(Louis - The Round the World Rug Race).

The layout stage.

Above: from the script, dummy pages are drawn.
There can be as few as one draft or as many as several dozen.

Right: a finished page of layout from Louis - Red Letter Day.
The next stages are pencilling (page 76), colouring (page 77), inking and lettering.

The original version of Louis - Red Letter Day.

Above and right: pages from the original version of Louis - Red Letter Day, created and published in 2000. Unlike the artwork for this book, the inking was done on separate pages from the colouring, then superimposed on computer.

Also by metaphrog:

Louis - Night Salad

Louis - Dreams Never Die
(graphic novel with music by hey and múm
on cd or blue vinyl + short animation)

Louis - The Clown's Last Words

Louis - Lying to Clive

Louis - Red Letter Day
(original version)

The Maze

Strange Weather Lately

The First Men on Mercury
(comic adaptation of the Edwin Morgan poem)

The Photographs

Skint!
(with playwright Gowan Calder)